Table of Contents

ESSENTIAL EARLY CHILDHOOD SKILLS

Everything for Early Learning is divided into five sections.

Basic Concepts

Activities in this section are designed to help your child:

- identify colors, basic shapes and sizes
- compare and describe the sizes and lengths of different objects
- classify objects according to common attributes
- understand the concept of opposites (in/out, up/down)
- understand positional concepts (behind, beside, between)
- develop and practice fine motor skills by coloring, cutting, gluing and manipulating objects

Mathematics Readiness

Activities in this section are designed to help your child:

- develop appropriate mathematical language
- match objects one-to-one
- develop concepts about quantity (more/fewer)
- develop general concepts about time (more time/less time)
- describe a simple sequence of events (before, after)
- describe events using ordinal numbers (first, second, third)

ESSENTIAL EARLY CHILDHOOD SKILLS

Reading Readiness

Activities in this section are designed to help your child:

- note similarities and differences among pictures, shapes, letters and words
- identify details that are missing from pictures
- identify parts of objects and the whole objects to which they belong
- identify rhymes in words and pictures
- follow directional paths from left to right and top to bottom
- form pre-writing strokes

Letters and Sounds

Activities in this section are designed to help your child:

- recognize and form the 26 upper- and lower-case letters of the alphabet
- identify the sound each letter makes at the beginning of a word

Numbers 0-10

Activities in this section are designed to help your child:

- recognize and write the numerals 0 to 10
- recognize and write number words from zero to ten
- count objects and sets of objects through ten

BASIC CONCEPTS

Color the pictures red.

BLUE

Color the pictures **blue**.

YELLOW

Color the pictures **yellow**.

ORANGE

Color the pictures **orange**.

GREEN

Color the pictures **green**.

BLACK

Color the pictures **black**.

Color the pictures **purple**.

BROWN

Color the pictures **brown**.

REVIEW COLORS

Color the picture.

REVIEW COLORS

Color the picture.

SORTING BY COLORS

Color and **cut out** the pictures at the bottom of the page. **Glue** the purple fruits in the purple basket. **Glue** the yellow fruits in the yellow basket. **Glue** the green fruits in the green basket.

Page is blank for cutting
exercise on previous page.

COLOR PATTERNS

Look at the beads in each row. **Color** the next bead in the **pattern**.

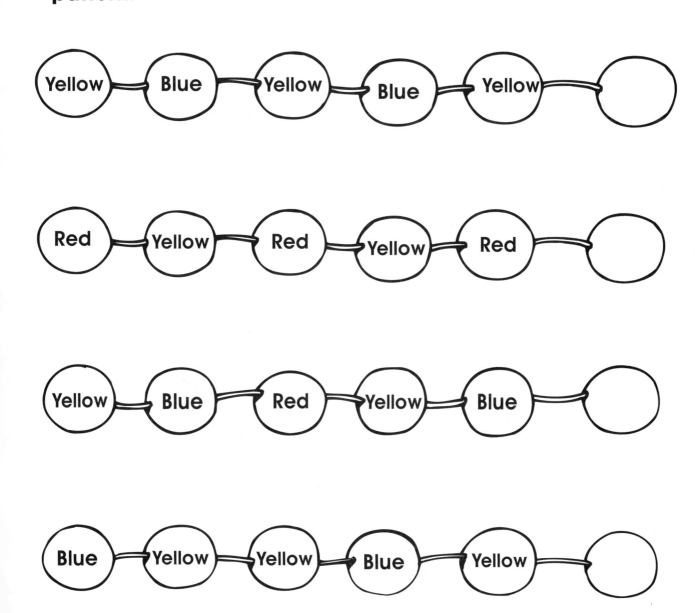

CIRCLES

We see many **circles** every day. **Trace** the circles. **Color** the pictures.

CIRCLES

Circles can be different sizes. **Trace** the **circles**. **Color** the **circles**.

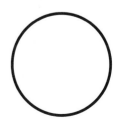

CIRCLES

Draw an **X** on the things that have the **shape** of a **circle**.
Color the picture.

SQUARES

We see many **squares** every day. **Squares** have 4 sides. **Trace** the **squares**. **Color** the pictures.

SQUARES

Squares can be different sizes. **Trace** the **squares**. **Color** the **squares**.

SQUARES

Draw an **X** on the things that have the **shape** of a **square**.
Color the picture.

RECTANGLES

We see many **rectangles** every day. **Rectangles** have 4 sides–2 long sides and 2 short sides. **Trace** the **rectangles**. **Color** the pictures.

RECTANGLES

Rectangles can be different sizes. **Trace** the
rectangles. **Color** the **rectangles**.

RECTANGLES

Draw an **X** on the things that have the **shape** of a **rectangle**. **Color** the pictures.

TRIANGLES

We see many **triangles** every day. **Triangles** have 3 sides. **Color** the **triangles**.

TRIANGLES

Triangles can be different sizes. **Color** the **triangles**.

TRIANGLES

Trace the **triangles. Color** the triangles.

TRIANGLES

Draw an **X** on the things that have the **shape** of a **triangle**.

SHAPES

Color the **shapes** to finish this picture.

Color the ■'s **yellow**. Color the ●'s **blue**.
Color the ▲'s **red**. Color the ■'s **green**.

Match the **shape patterns** on the **left** with the **shape patterns** on the **right**.

Look at the **shapes** in each row. **Draw** the next **shape** in the pattern.

REVIEW SHAPES

circle   rectangle   triangle   square

Name the **shape** at the beginning of each row.
Circle the other **shape** in that row that is the same.

Look at all the **shapes**.

Color the ■'s **yellow**.

Color the ▲'s **red**.

Color the ●'s **blue**.

Color the ▬'s **green**.

Draw a line from the **circle** to each thing that has the shape of a **circle**. Draw a line from the **square** to each thing that has the shape of a **square**.

SORTING BY SHAPE

Draw a line from the **rectangle** to each thing that has the shape of a **rectangle**. **Draw** a line from the **triangle** to each thing that has the shape of a **triangle**.

TRIANGLES

5LZ-62F

RECTANGLES

Draw a **line** to the matching **shapes**.

Look at the **shapes**. **Draw** the **shape** that comes next in the pattern.

REVIEW COLORS AND SHAPES

Color each **square blue**. **Color** each **circle green**.
Color each **triangle brown**. Then, finish the picture
with your favorite colors!

Some things are **big**. Some things are **small**. **Circle** the things that are **small**.

Sizes

 Circle the things that are **small**.

Sizes

 Circle the things that are **big**.

Sizes

Which one is **big**? **Circle** the one that is **big**.
Color the pictures.

Look at the pictures in the box. **Color** the **small** pictures **green**.
Color the **big** pictures **yellow**.

Look at the pictures in the box. **Color** the **small** pictures **red**. **Color** the **big** pictures **purple**.

Sizes

Circle the **biggest** thing. Draw an **X** on the **smallest** thing.

Circle the **smallest** thing. **Draw** an **X** on the **biggest** thing.

Color the pictures. ✂ **Cut out** the boxes. Put them in order from

SMALLEST to BIGGEST

Page is blank for cutting
exercise on previous page.

Sizes

Some things are **long**. Some things are **short**. **Circle** the things that are **long**.

Sizes

Which one is **long**? **Circle** the thing that is **long**. **Color** the pictures.

LONG

Sizes

Look at the pictures in each box. **Circle** the things that are **short**. **Color** the pictures.

SHORT

Which one is **short**? **Circle** the thing that is **short**. **Color** the pictures.

Sizes

Circle the **longest** thing in each row. LONG LONGER LONGEST

Circle the **shortest** thing in each row.

Sizes

Circle the **longest** thing in each row. **Draw** an **X** on the **shortest** thing.

Some things are **tall**. Some things are **short**. **Circle** the things that are **short**.

Look at the pictures in each box. **Circle** the people who are **tall**. **Color** the pictures.

TALL

Sizes

Circle the **tallest** thing in each row.

Sizes

Circle the **shortest** thing in each row.

SHORT SHORTER SHORTEST

Sizes

Circle the **tallest** thing in each row. **Draw** an **X** on the **shortest** thing.

Color, **cut out** and **glue**. Put the goat going up the mountain.

Do not cut.
Activity on other side.

Color, **cut out** and **glue**. Put the bunny going **down** the slide.

DOWN

Do not cut.
Activity on other side.

Color and **cut out** the **children**. **Glue** one child **up** at the **top** of the slide. **Glue** the other child **down** at the **bottom** of the slide.

Page is blank for cutting
exercise on previous page.

Color, **cut out** and **glue**. Put the school bell on top of the schoolhouse.

Do not cut.
Activity on other side.

Color, **cut out** and **glue**. Put the drum on the bottom shelf.

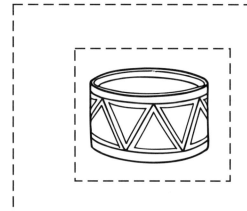

Do not cut.
Activity on other side.

Color and **cut out** the balls. **Glue** one ball on the **top** stair.
Glue the other ball on the **bottom** stair.

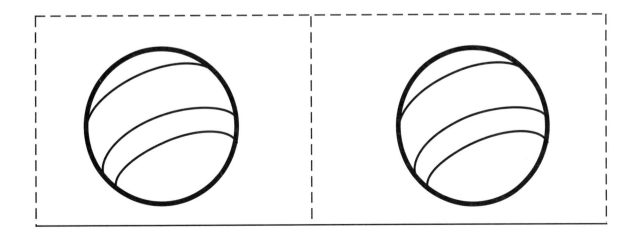

Page is blank for cutting
exercise on previous page.

Color, **cut out** and **glue**. Put the teddy bear **on** the bed.

ON

Do not cut.
Activity on other side.

Color, **cut out** and **glue**. Put the lamp shade on the lamp that is **off**.

Do not cut.
Activity on other side.

Position Words

Color and **cut out** the bears. **Glue** one bear **on** the box. **Glue** the other bear **off** the box.

©2001 McGraw-Hill. All Rights Reserved.

Page is blank for cutting
exercise on previous page.

Position Words

Color, **cut out** and **glue**. Put the plane **over** the cloud.

OVER

Do not cut.
Activity on other side.

Color, cut out and **glue**. Put the bear **under** the beehive.

UNDER

Do not cut.
Activity on other side.

Position Words

Color and **cut out** the birds. **Glue** one bird **over** the rainbow.
Glue the other bird **under** the rainbow.

Page is blank for cutting
exercise on previous page.

Color, **cut out** and **glue**. Put the mouse **inside** the mouse hole.

INSIDE

*Do not cut.
Activity on other side.*

Color, **cut out** and **glue**. Put the bat **outside** the bat cave.

OUTSIDE

Do not cut.
Activity on other side.

Color, **cut out** and **glue**. Put the rows of flowers in **front** of the house.

Do not cut.
Activity on other side.

Position Words

  Color, **cut out** and **glue**. Put the toy into the **back** of the wagon.

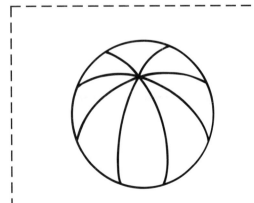

Do not cut.
Activity on other side.

Position Words

Color, **cut out** and **glue**. Put the rocket **below** the moon.

Do not cut.
Activity on other side.

Color, **cut out** and **glue**. Put the spaceship **above** the stars.

ABOVE

*Do not cut.
Activity on other side.*

Which tea cup is **nearest** to the teapot? **Color** the picture.

NEAREST

Which skunk hit the ball the **farthest**? **Color** the picture.

FARTHEST

Position Words

  Color, **cut out** and **glue**. Put the chicken **beside** the barn.

BESIDE

Do not cut.
Activity on other side.

Color, **cut out** and **glue**. Put the cart **behind** the horse.

BEHIND

Do not cut.
Activity on other side.

Color, **cut out** and **glue**. Put the basket of fruit **between** the trees.

BETWEEN

Do not cut.
Activity on other side.

Page is blank for cutting
exercise on previous page.

Color, **cut out** and **glue**. Put the ballerina's slipper on her **right** foot.

RIGHT

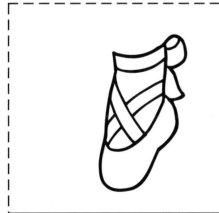

Do not cut.
Activity on other side.

Color, **cut out** and **glue**. Put the mitt on the baseball player's **left** hand.

LEFT

Do not cut.
Activity on other side.

Draw a line to match the **things that go together**.

MATCH

Draw a line to match the **things that go together**.

Look at the pictures below. **Draw** a picture to show something else that can go with each group.

GROUPS

Things for **Warm** Weather

Things for **Cold** Weather

Things for **Rainy** Weather

WHERE DOES IT GO?

Help put things in the right place in the house. **Cut out** the pictures at the **bottom** of the page. **Glue** the kitchen things in the kitchen. **Glue** the bedroom things in the bedroom.

GREAT JOB!

COOL!

Fantastic!

WOW!

WAY TO GO!

WHAT BELONGS?

Color the pictures in each row that belong together.
Draw an **X** on the one that **does not** belong.

MATHEMATICS READINESS

 + **= 4**

Draw a **line** from each animal to its home.

Look at the pictures in each box. **Draw** a line from each animal to its home.

Look at the pictures in each box. **Draw** a **line** to match each thing at the **top** to the thing at the **bottom**. **Color** the pictures.

Look at the animals. **Draw** a ball for **each** animal. **Color** the pictures.

ONE-TO-ONE

SAME NUMBER

Each pond has the **same number** of ducks in it. **Color** the ducks.

Draw kites so that Sue will have the **same number** as Billy.

More and Fewer

Match the pictures. **Circle** the group that has **more**.

More and Fewer

Look at the pictures in each box. **Circle** the group that has **more**. **Color** the pictures.

More and Fewer

Match the pictures. **Circle** the group that has **fewer**.

More and Fewer

Look at the pictures in each box. Circle the group that has fewer. Color the pictures.

FEWER

MORE and FEWER

more

fewer

1. **Color** the group that has **more**.

2. **Color** the group that has **fewer**.

Sequence

What happened **before**? **Circle** the **small** picture that shows what happened **before** the pictures in the boxes.

Sequence

Look at the pictures. Which happened **first** in each row?
Circle the picture that shows what
happened **first**.

FIRST

Sequence

Circle the thing that happened **first** in each row.

Sequence

What comes **next**? **Look** at the big pictures. **Circle** the small picture that shows what would happen **next**.

Sequence

Draw a line from the picture on the left to the picture which happens **next**.

NEXT

Look at the pictures. What happened **first**? What happened **second**? What happened **third**? **Draw** a line from the correct word to the picture.

first

second

third

Cut out the pictures and **glue** them to show what happened **first**, **second** and **third**.

FIRST SECOND THIRD

Glue

Page is blank for cutting
exercise on previous page.

Sequence

How does a plant grow? **Cut out** the pictures. **Glue** the pictures in the boxes to show what happens **first**, **second** and **third**.

FIRST SECOND THIRD

Page is blank for cutting
exercise on previous page.

Sequence

Write **1**, **2** and **3** in the boxes to show what happens **first**, **second** and **third**.

FIRST SECOND THIRD

REVIEW

Circle the picture that shows what comes **next**.

Time

Some things take a **little time**. Some things take **a lot of time**. **Color** each picture that takes **more** time.

MORE

Time

Color the picture that would take **more** time to do.

Time

Circle the picture in each row that takes **more** time.

Circle the picture in each row that takes **more** time.

When you eat an ice-cream cone, it is gone in **a short time**. **Color** the picture of the job which takes **less time to do**.

Color the picture of the job which takes **less time to do**.

NUMBERS 0 – 10

NUMBER 0

This is 0.
Color the number. **Color** the word.

NUMBER 1

This is 1.
Color the number. **Color** the word.
Color the rest of the picture.

one

NUMBER 1

Count and **color**.

Color I **red,** I **blue and** I **green. Circle** each group of **1**.

NUMBER 1

1 ball is colored.

Color **1** ball.

Trace the number. **Write** the number on the line **one** time.

NUMBER 2

This is 2.

Color the number. **Color** the word.
Count and **color** the rest of the picture.

TWO

NUMBER 2

Count and **color**. **Color** the flowers: **2 red**, **2 purple** and **2 yellow**.
Circle each with a **2**.

NUMBER 2

2 fish are colored.

Color **2** fish.

Trace the number. **Write** the number on the lines **two** times.

2

NUMBERS 1 AND 2

Circle groups of **1**. **Color** each group of **2**.

1

2

NUMBERS 1 AND 2

Write the numbers **1** and **2**.

Draw 1 ball on the seal's nose.

Draw 2 balls on the seal's nose.

NUMBER 3

This is 3.
Color the number. **Color** the word.
Count and **color** the rest of the picture.

NUMBER 3

Count and **color** the pictures. **Circle** each group of **3**.

NUMBER 3

3 birds are colored.

Color 3 birds.

Trace the number. **Write** the number on the lines **three** times.

NUMBER 4

This is 4.
Color the number. Color the word.
Count and color the rest of the picture.

NUMBER 4

Circle each group of **4**. **Color** the picture.

©2001 McGraw-Hill. All Rights Reserved.

141

4 cats are **colored**.

Color 4 cats.

Trace the number. **Write** the number on the lines **four** times.

4 — — — — — — — —

NUMBERS 3 AND 4

Circle groups of **3**. **Color** each group of **4**.

3

4

NUMBERS 3 AND 4

Write the numbers **3** and **4**.

3 3

4 4

Draw 3 scoops of ice cream on the cone.

Draw 4 scoops of ice cream on the cone.

This is 5.
Color the number. **Color** the word.
Count and **color** the rest of the picture.

NUMBER 5

Count and **color** each picture. **Circle** each group of **5**.

NUMBER 5

5 dogs are **colored**.

Color 5 dogs.

Trace the number. **Write** the number on the lines **five** times.

5 _____ _____ _____ _____ _____

Review
NUMBERS 0-5

How Many?

Circle the number of things below. **Color** the pictures.

1 2 3

2 3 4

3 4 5

1 2 3

Review NUMBERS 0-5

How Many?

Circle the number of things below. **Color** the pictures.

2   3   4

3   4   5

1   2   3

3   4   5

Review
NUMBERS 0-5

Count each group of fruit. **Write** the number in the box.
Color the fruit, too.

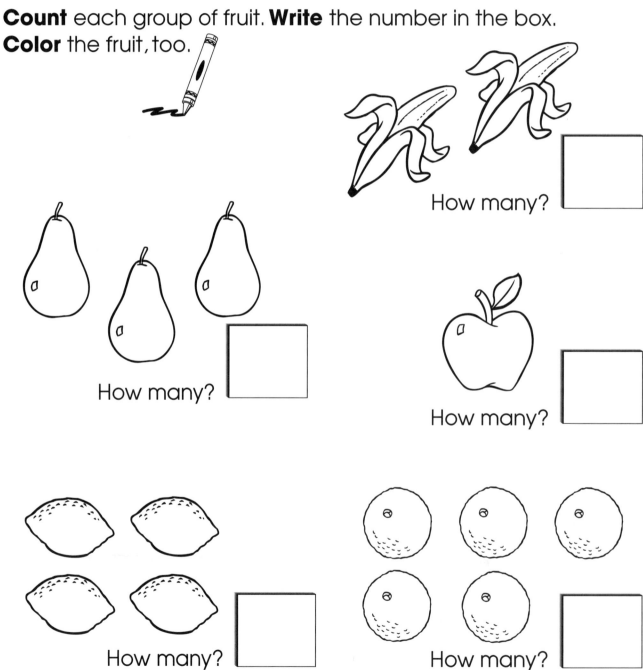

How many?

How many?

How many?

How many?

How many?

Review
NUMBERS 0-5

Count and **color** each group of animals. **Cut out** and **glue** the numbers.

Page is blank for cutting
exercise on previous page.

NUMBER 6

This is 6.
Color the number. **Color** the word.
Count and **color** the rest of the picture.

NUMBER 6

Count and color each picture. Circle each group of 6.

NUMBER 6

Circle each group of **6**.

NUMBERS 5 AND 6

Write the numbers **5** and **6**.

5 5 _ _ _ _ _ _ _ _ _ _ _ 6 6 _ _ _ _ _ _ _ _ _ _ _

Draw 5 coins in the piggy bank.   **Draw 6** coins in the piggy bank.

NUMBER 7

This is 7.

Color the number. **Color** the word.
Count and **color** the rest of the picture.

NUMBER 7

Count and **color** each picture. **Circle** each group of **7**.

NUMBER 7

Write the number **7**.

7 7 - - - - - - - - - - - - - - - -

Count and **color**.

Draw 7 peas on the plate.

This is 8.

Color the number. **Color** the word.

Count and **color** the rest of the picture.

NUMBER 8

Color the spaces: **8 = yellow** **= red** **eight = green**

NUMBER 8

Write the number **8**.

8 8

Count and **color**.

Draw 8 spots on the bug's back.

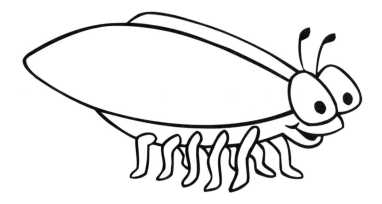

NUMBERS 7 AND 8

Circle groups of **7**. **Color** each group of **8**.

NUMBER 9

This is 9.

Color the number. **Color** the word.
Count and **color** the rest of the picture.

NUMBER 9

Count and **color** each picture. **Circle** each group of **9**.

NUMBER 9

Write the number **9**.

9 9

Count and **color**.

___
- - - - -
___

Draw 9 ice-cream scoops on the cones.

NUMBER 10

This is 10.

Color the number. **Color** the word.
Count and **color** the rest of the picture.

NUMBER 10

Where are the **10**'s? **Circle** the **10**'s with **red**. **Color** the picture.
How many 🦋 's?

Write the number **10**.

10 10

Count and **color**.

_____

- - - - -

_____

Draw 10 triangles on the snake's back.

NUMBERS 9 AND 10

Circle groups of **9**. **Color** each group of **10**.

9

10

Review
NUMBERS 0-10

Count the pictures in each group. **Circle** the number. **Color** the pictures.

8   3   5

2   6   I

3   7   9

6   8   4

3   8   2

5   10   6

Review
NUMBERS 0-10

Count the pictures in each group. **Circle** the number. **Color** the pictures.

5 4 6

3 7 10

2 9 8

6 4 1

4 5 7

3 8 9

Review NUMBERS 0-10

Too Many Objects

Draw an **X** on the extra things in each row.

Review
NUMBERS 0-10

Connect the dots from **1** to **10**. **Color** the picture.

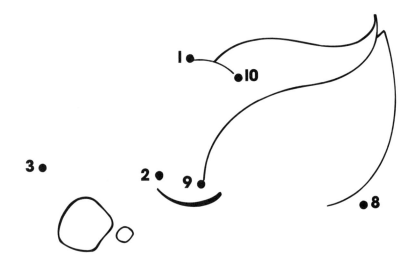

1 ●
● 10

3 ●

2 ● 9 ●

● 8

4 ●

● 7

5 ●
● 6

Review NUMBERS 0-10

Connect the dots from **1** to **10**. **Color** the picture.

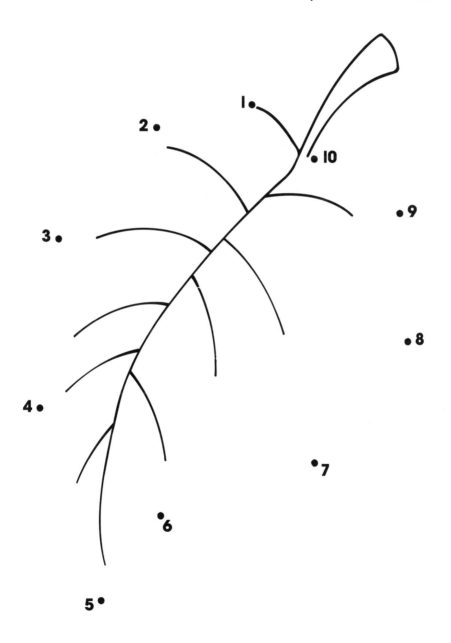

Review
NUMBERS 0-10

Connect the dots from **1** to **10**. **Color** the picture.

Review
NUMBERS 0-10

Connect the dots from **1** to **10**. **Draw** and **color** a picture on Teddy's shirt.

Decorate my shirt!

READING READINESS

Same and Different

Color the pictures in each row that are the **same**.

Same and Different

Color the pictures in each row that are the **same**.

Same and Different

Color the pictures in each row that are the **same**.

Circle each picture that is the **same** as the **first** picture in the row.

Same and Different

1. **Cut out** the picture cards below.
2. Put the cards in a bag. Shake the bag.
3. Pull out two cards.
4. If the pictures are the **same**, keep them.
5. If the pictures are **not the same**, put them back in the bag and try again.

Page is blank for cutting
exercise on previous page.

Same and Different

Color the **picture** in each row that is **different**.

Same and Different

Circle the **picture** in each row that is **different**.

Colors and Shapes

Circle the puzzle piece in each row that is **different**.

Same and Different

Circle the **picture** in each row that is **different**.

Same and Different

Look at the picture in each box. **Circle** the picture of the thing it **comes from**.

COMES FROM

Same and Different

Look at the pictures of the musical instruments. **Draw** the missing parts.

WHAT IS MISSING?

Same and Different

Play a matching game with cookies!

1. **Cut out** the cards.
2. Put the cards letter side down on the tray. Mix them up.
3. Turn over two cards at a time. If they match, keep the cards. If not, put them back on the tray.
4. Play until no cards are left.

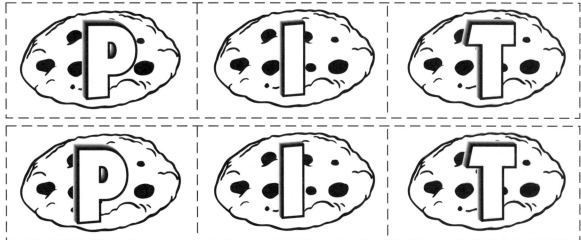

Page is blank for cutting
exercise on previous page.

Same and Different

Look at the letters below. **Draw** an **X** on the letter in each row that is **different**.

DIFFERENT

Same and Different

Circle the two letters in each row of blocks that are the **same**.
The first row shows you what to do.

SAME

Same and Different

Look at the words below. **Circle** the two words in each row that are the **same**. The first one shows you what to do.

SAME

be   to   be

in   do   in

at   at   go

is   am   am

Look at the words below. **Circle** the word that is the **same** as the first word in the row. The first one shows you what to do.

SAME

bug. | bug | mug

bat | bat | mat

pin | tin | pin

jam | ham | jam

Rhymes

Look at the picture of the **cat**. **Draw** a **line** from the **cat** to each picture that **rhymes** with the word **cat**. One is done for you. **Color** the pictures.

RHYMES

Look at the picture of the **bug**. **Draw** a **line** from the **bug** to each picture that **rhymes** with the word **bug**. **Color** the pictures.

RHYMES

Look at the picture of the **pail**. **Draw** a **line** from the **pail** to each picture that **rhymes** with the word **pail**. **Color** the pictures.

RHYMES

Look at the **first picture** in each row. **Circle** the picture that **rhymes** with it. **Color** the pictures.

RHYMES

Rhymes

Look at the **first picture** in each row. **Circle** the picture that **rhymes** with it. **Color** the pictures.

Look at the **first picture** in each row. **Circle** the picture that **rhymes** with it. **Color** the pictures.

RHYMES

Look at the **first picture** in each row. **Circle** the picture that **rhymes** with it. **Color** the pictures.

RHYMES

Draw a **line** to match each **rhyming** picture. **Color** the pictures.

Draw a **line** to match each **rhyming** picture. **Color** the pictures.

Draw a **line** to match each **rhyming** picture. **Color** the pictures.

Draw a **line** to match each **rhyming** picture. **Color** the pictures.

RHYMES

Left-to-Right

Trace the paths from the pictures on the **left** to some places to play on the **right**. The first one is done for you.

Help the **ants** get back to the **picnic baskets**!

209

Left-to-Right

Help the **fish** get back into the **water**!

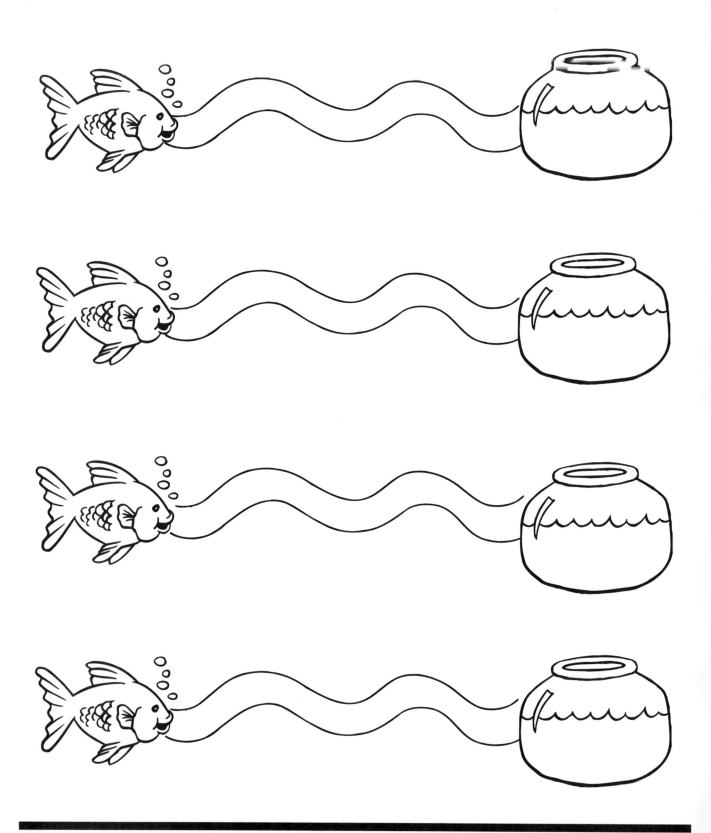

Help the **bunnies** get their **carrots**!

Trace the dotted line. **Start** at the **left** and go to the **right**.

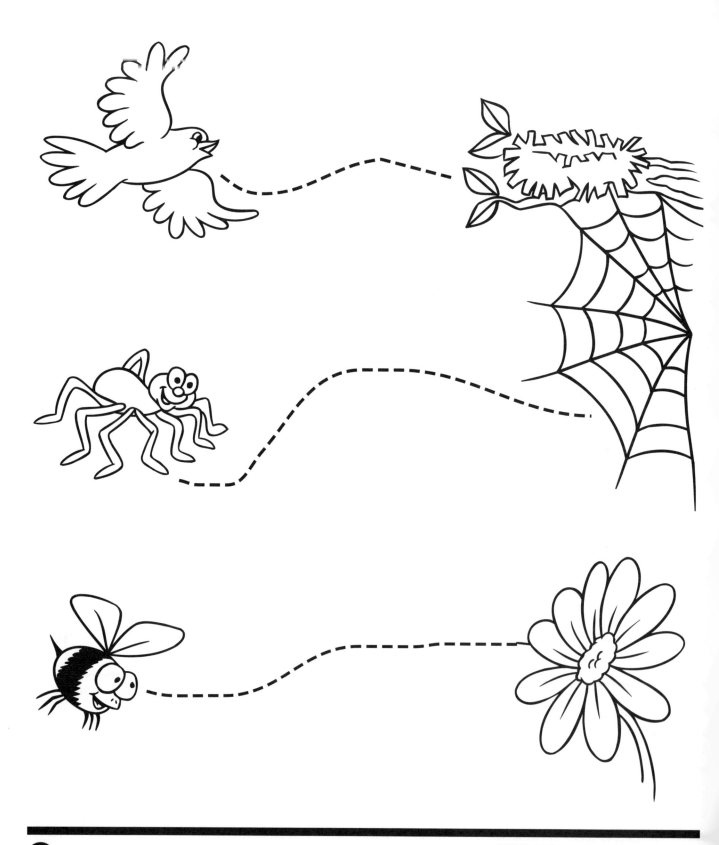

Help the **birds** fly to the **clouds**!

Beginning Writing Skills

Start at the **dots**. **Trace** the **dotted** lines.

Start at the **dots**. **Trace** the **dotted** lines.

Start at the **dots**. **Trace** the **dotted** lines.

Start at the **dots**. **Trace** the **dotted** lines.

Beginning Writing Skills

Start at the **dots**. **Trace** the **dotted** lines.

Beginning Writing Skills

Start at the **dots**. **Trace** the **dotted** lines.

Start at the **dots**. **Trace** the **dotted** lines.

Beginning Writing Skills

Start at the **dots**. **Trace** the **dotted** lines.

LETTERS AND SOUNDS

Letter

Upper-case

Trace the letters.

Letter

Lower-case

Trace the letters.

Letter

Draw a line to follow the letters **A** and **a**.
Color the picture.

Circle the pictures that start with the sound of **Aa**.

Color the pictures.

Letters and Sounds

Letter
B
Upper-case

Trace the letters.

Letter
b
Lower-case

Trace the letters.

Letter Bb

Find each hidden **B** and **b**.

Draw a **blue circle** around each **B**.
Draw an **orange circle** around each **b**.

Letter Bb

Circle the pictures that start with the sound of **Bb**.

Color the pictures.

BOOK

Letter

C

Upper-case

Trace the letters.

Letter

C

Lower-case

Trace the letters.

Letter

Find each **C** and **c** that the cat has made with the yarn.

Color the **UPPER-case C's red.**
Color the lower-case c's yellow.

Letter Cc

Circle the pictures that start with the sound of **Cc**.

Color the pictures.

Letter
D
Upper-case

Trace the letters.

Letter
d
Lower-case

Trace the letters.

Color the spaces with the letters **D** or **d** **purple**.

Color spaces with the other letters **orange**.

What did you find?

Color the doll, too!

Letter Dd

Circle the pictures that start with the sound of **Dd**.

Color the pictures.

Letter

E

Upper-case

Trace the letters.

Letter

e

Lower-case

Trace the letters.

Letter
Ee

Help the 🐘 find his way to the circus tent.

Color the 🥜's with **E** or **e brown**.
Color the other 🥜's **green**.
Color the picture!

Letters and Sounds

Circle the pictures that start with the sound of **Ee**.

Color the pictures.

Letter

F

Upper-case

Trace the letters.

Letter

f

Lower-case

Trace the letters.

Letter Ff

Color and **cut out** each picture that starts with the sound of **Ff**. **Glue** them on the fence.

Page is blank for cutting
exercise on previous page.

Circle the pictures that start with the sound of **Ff**.

Color the pictures.

Letter
G
Upper-case

Trace the letters.

Letter
g
Lower-case

Trace the letters.

Letter Gg

Look at each sign in the garden.

Trace each **G** and **g**.

Color each sign with **G red**.
Color each sign with **g blue**.

How many?

I have
_____ G's
_____ g's

Letter Gg

Circle the pictures that start with the sound of **Gg**.

Color the pictures.

WELCOME

Letter

H

Upper-case

Trace the letters.

Letter

h

Lower-case

Trace the letters.

Color the spaces with the **UPPER-case H red**.

Color the spaces with the **lower-case h purple**.

What did you find?

Letter Hh

Circle the pictures that start with the sound of **Hh.**

Color the pictures.

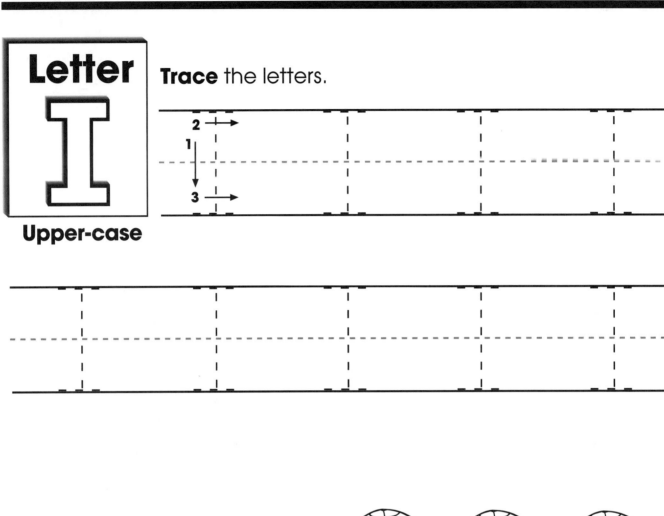

Letter

Upper-case

Trace the letters.

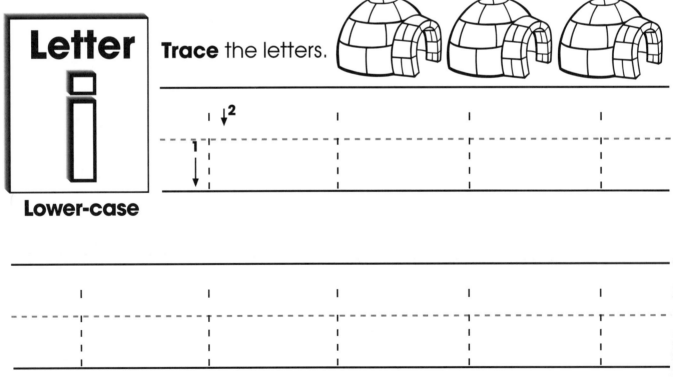

Letter

Lower-case

Trace the letters.

Letter
Ii

Help read the 's smoke signals.

Color each **I** **red**. **Color** each **i** **orange**.

Color the picture!

Letter Ii

Circle the pictures that start with the sound of **Ii**.

Color the pictures.

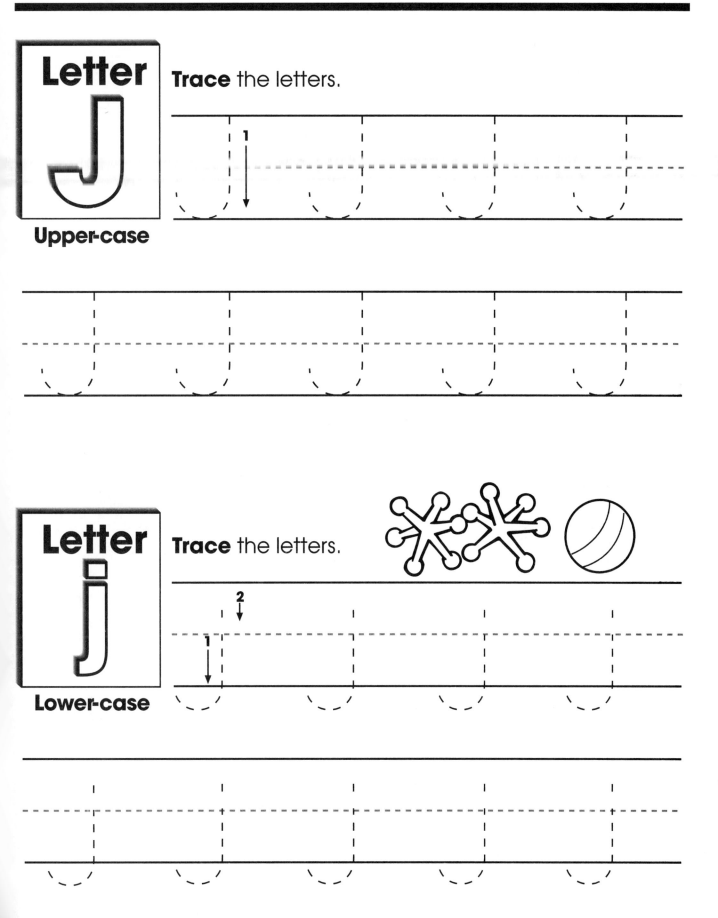

Letter
J

Upper-case

Trace the letters.

Letter
j

Lower-case

Trace the letters.

Letter Jj

Can you **find** each hidden **J** and **j** in the picture?

Color each **J red**.
Color each **J green.**
Then, **color** the rest of the picture!

Circle the pictures that start with the sound of **Jj**.

Color the pictures.

Draw a line to match the **UPPER-case** and **lower-case** letters that belong together.

**Review
Letters**

Draw a line to match the **UPPER-case** and **lower-case** letters that belong together.

Letter

K

Upper-case

Trace the letters.

Letter

k

Lower-case

Trace the letters.

Letter Kk

Look at each letter on the kites.

Match the letters on the kites and **color** them the correct colors.

K = blue
k = yellow

K = yellow
k = red

K = orange
k = purple

K = green
k = red

Circle the pictures that start with the sound of **Kk**.

Color the pictures.

Letters and Sounds

Letter L
Upper-case

Trace the letters.

Letter l
Lower-case

Trace the letters.

Letter
LI

It is fun to rake the fall leaves!

Color the leaves with **L orange**.
Color the leaves with **I red**.

Letter

Circle the pictures that start with the sound of **Ll**.

Color the pictures.

Letter

M

Upper-case

Trace the letters.

Letter

m

Lower-case

Trace the letters.

Letter

Draw a line from each to a picture which starts with the sound of **Mm**.

Letter

Mm

Circle the pictures that start with the sound of **Mm**.

Color the pictures.

Letter
N
Upper-case

Trace the letters.

Letter
n
Lower-case

Trace the letters.

Can you **find** each **N** and **n** that is hidden in the room?

Color each **N purple**. **Color** each **n orange**.

Then, **color** the rest of the picture!

Circle the pictures that start with the sound of **Nn**.

Color the pictures.

Letter

Upper-case

Trace the letters.

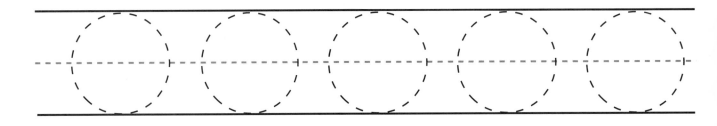

Letter

Lower-case

Trace the letters.

Letter

O o

See who has 8 legs and lives in the ocean.

Color the spaces with **O** or **o brown**.
Color the other spaces **blue**.

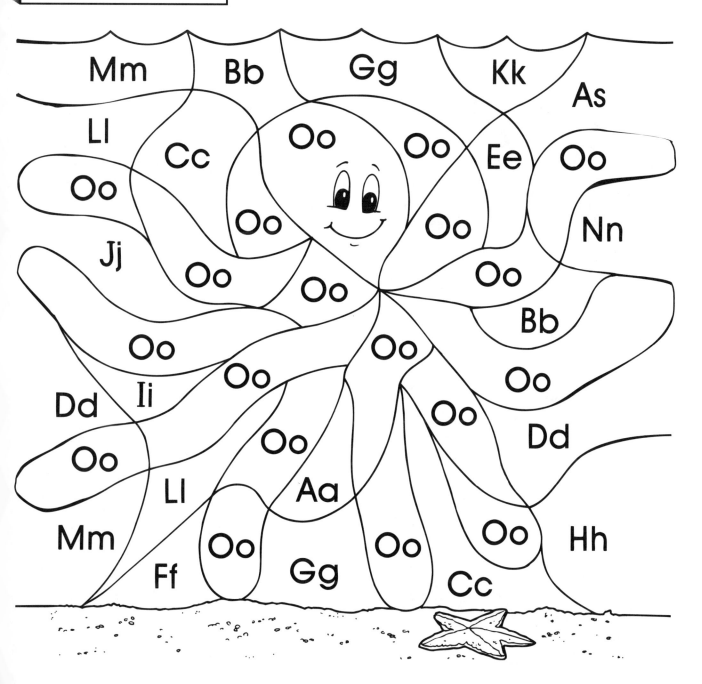

Letter

Oo

Circle the pictures that start with the sound of **Oo**.

Color the pictures.

Review Letters
A-O

The Mouse on the Moon

Connect the dots from **A-O**.

Color the picture.

What do you see?

Review Letters
A-O

Connect the dots from **a-o** as you **say the alphabet**.

Color the picture.

Start with the letter **a**.

Alphabet Camping

Trace the letters on the tent.

Color the picture!

273

Letter

P

Upper-case

Trace the letters.

Letter

p

Lower-case

Trace the letters.

Trace each **Pp**. Then, **color** each pepperoni **red**.

Cut out each pepperoni and **glue** it on the pizza.

Page is blank for cutting
exercise on previous page.

Letter Pp

Circle the pictures that start with the sound of **Pp**.

Color the pictures.

PENCIL

Letter
Q

Upper-case

Trace the letters.

Letter
q

Lower-case

Trace the letters.

Look how quiet everything is in the library!

Can you **find** each **Q** and **q**?

Color each **Q blue**.
Color each **q yellow**.

Letter Qq

Circle the pictures that start with the sound of **Qq**.

Color the pictures.

Letter

R

Upper-case

Trace the letters.

Letter

r

Lower-case

Trace the letters.

Letter

Rr

Trace each **R** and **r**.

Color each raindrop with **R green**.
Color each raindrop with **r blue**.
Color the umbrella, too!

Letter

Circle the pictures that start with the sound of **Rr**.

Color the pictures.

Letter

S

Upper-case

Trace the letters.

Letter

S

Lower-case

Trace the letters.

Letter Ss

Trace each **S** and **s**.

Color each bubble with **S yellow**.
Color each bubble with **s purple**.

Soap

Circle the pictures that start with the sound of **Ss**.

Color the pictures.

Letter

Upper-case

Trace the letters.

Letter

Lower-case

Trace the letters.

Color the pictures that start with the sound of **Tt**.

Letter Tt

Circle the pictures that start with the sound of **Tt**.

Color the pictures.

Review Letters A-T

What is the Rabbit Queen jumping out of?

Connect the dots and you will see!

Color the picture.

Review Letters A-T

Follow the maze and **say** each letter. Start with **A** for ant and end with **T** for turtle.

Color the picture!

Letter

Upper-case

Trace the letters.

Letter

Lower-case

Trace the letters.

Letter Uu

Find each hidden **U** and **u**.

Color each **U** purple.
Color each **u** orange.
Color the picture.

Letter Uu

Circle the pictures that start with the sound of **Uu**.

Color the pictures.

Letter

Upper-case

Trace the letters.

Letter

Lower-case

Trace the letters.

Letter Vv

Circle the pictures that start with the sound of **Vv**.

Color the pictures.

Letter Vv

Trace each **V** and **v**.
Color each heart with **V** or **v** red.
 Cut out and glue **glue** each
V and **v** on a bigger heart.

Page is blank for cutting
exercise on previous page.

Letter

Upper-case

Trace the letters.

Letter

Lower-case

Trace the letters.

Circle the pictures that start with the sound of **Ww**.

Color the pictures.

Letter Ww

Color each watch.
Color and ✂ **cut out** each picture
that starts with **Ww**.
Then, **glue** 🏺 them on the watches.

Page is blank for cutting
exercise on previous page.

Letter

X

Upper-case

Trace the letters.

Letter

X

Lower-case

Trace the letters.

Circle the pictures that start with the letter **Xx**.

Color the pictures.

Letter Xx

Color the **UPPER-case X's red**.
Color the **lower-case x's blue**.
✂ **Cut out** and 🧴 **glue** each **X**
and **x**. Put an **UPPER-case X** and a
lower-case x in each set.

Page is blank for cutting
exercise on previous page.

Letter

Y

Upper-case

Trace the letters.

Letter

y

Lower-case

Trace the letters.

Letter
Yy

Find each **Y** and **y** hidden in the yard.

Color each **Y** red.
Color each **y** yellow.

Circle the pictures that start with the sound of **Yy**.

Color the pictures.

Letter

Z

Upper-case

Trace the letters.

Letter

Z

Lower-case

Trace the letters.

Letter Z z

Take a trip through the zoo.

Color only the pictures that start with the sound of **Zz**.

Zoo

Letter Zz

Circle the pictures that start with the sound of **Zz**.

Color the pictures.

Connect the dots as you **say the alphabet**.
Color the picture!

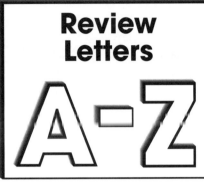

Review Letters A-Z

Connect the dots from **A** to **Z**.

Color the gumballs your favorite colors!

Letters and Sounds

Review Letters A-Z

Color and **cut out** the alphabet cards. Use them as flash cards or practice putting your **ABC**'s in order.

Aa

Bb

Cc

Dd

Ee

Ff

Gg

Hh

Ii

Page is blank for cutting
exercise on previous page.

Review Letters

A-Z

Color and **cut out** the alphabet cards. Use them as flash cards or practice putting your **ABC**'s in order.

Page is blank for cutting
exercise on previous page.

Review Letters

Color and **cut out** the alphabet cards. Use them as flash cards or practice putting your **ABC**'s in order.

Page is blank for cutting
exercise on previous page.